Lara McKenzie is a former management consultant and now works as an analyst. Her first book, a memoir called *Virtual Insanity*, was published in 2020. She is also the author of a children's book, *Wizard Company*, published in 2021. Lara comes from a long line of family members who have served their country in the infantry.

LEST
WE FORGET

Lara McKenzie

Austin Macauley Publishers™
LONDON ★ CAMBRIDGE ★ NEW YORK ★ SHARJAH

Copyright © Lara McKenzie (2021)

A CIP catalogue record for this title is available from the British Library.

ISBN 9781398409316 (Paperback)
ISBN 9781398409330 (ePub e-book)

www.austinmacauley.com

First Published (2021)
Austin Macauley Publishers Ltd
25 Canada Square
Canary Wharf
London
E14 5LQ

To Hannah and Joshua, my wonderful children, I am so proud of both of you.

To Lukasz, thank you for your love and support. To Bill, Mum, your support is everything to me.

To Dad and Jane, with love always.

Remembering the Katyn Massacre of the Polish Military Officers and Intelligentsia, 1940. Poland, Lest We Forget.

To those past and present who serve, and have served, in our Armed Forces. Thank you for eternity.

"Mamma," said Frankie, "what does 'Lest We Forget' mean?"

"It means not to forget past sacrifices," said Mother. "It's a remembrance saying for those who have served in war who protect us and our way of life."

"Like Daddy does?" said Frankie.

"Yes," said Mother, "it is also used in war remembrance services and commemorative events. Like what we went to on the 11th of November. Remembrance Day. It's called Armistice Day."

"What does Armistice Day mean?" asked Frankie.

"Well, Armistice Day is Remembrance Day on the 11th of November each year. It's the day World War One ended at 11 a.m. on the 11th day of the 11th month in 1918, a long time ago."

"And why do we have to be silent on Armistice Day?" asked Frankie?

"A two-minute silence is held at 11 a.m. to remember the people who have died in wars."

"Yes Mamma. We went with Daddy and I remembered," said Frankie.

11 November
Remembrance Day
Lest We Forget

"And the poppy, Mamma?" said Frankie.

"The poppy is to remember them, all those soldiers, navy men and air force personnel who fought in World War One and World War Two and conflicts thereafter. It's the flower used to remember them. Each day on the 11th of November each year, people wear them. They also wear them on ANZAC Day."

"What is ANZAC Day?" said Frankie.

"Well ANZAC stands for Australia and New Zealand Army Corps. It's from World War One and is the national day of remembrance in Australia and New Zealand that remembers Australians and New Zealanders who served and died in all wars and conflicts and peacekeeping operations. ANZAC Day is on the 25th of April, but most English-speaking countries commemorate Remembrance Day on the 11th of November each year."

"Now I have to tell you more about this phrase 'Lest We Forget'," said Mother.

"Tell me, Mamma," said Frankie.

"Well the words 'Lest We Forget' were first used in a Christian poem by a poet named Rudyard Kipling in 1897. The poem was called 'Recessional'. The poem says:

'God of our fathers, known of old,
Lord of our far-flung battle line,
Beneath whose awful hand we hold
Dominion over palm and pine—
Lord God of Hosts, be with us yet,
Lest we forget—lest we forget!'

"So that's where it originally comes from," said Mother. "Wow," said Frankie, "but I don't really like poems, Mamma!"

"I'll tell you one more thing about it too," said Mother. "It's also a phrase that's present in the Bible."

"The Bible?" asked Frankie.

"Yes, in Deuteronomy 4:7-9. And it says in the Bible 'lest thou forget the things thine eyes have seen.'"

"Mamma," said Frankie, "why does Daddy have angel wings on his uniform?"

"Well that's his uniform as a Royal Air Force pilot. Wings like an angel flying."

"I want to be an air force pilot like Daddy, Mamma."

"I know," said Mother. "Per ardua ad astra."

"What does that mean?" said Frankie.

"It's the Royal Air Force motto. It is the motto of the Royal Australian Air Force and Royal New Zealand Air Force too."

"But what does it mean?" asked Frankie.

"It's in Latin. It means 'through adversity, to the stars' or 'through struggle to the stars'."

"One more question, Mamma," said Frankie. "When's Daddy coming home?"

"Come and sit on my lap," said Mother, "he will be home in five weeks and then it will be Remembrance Day and we will remember them together at the 11th hour on the 11th day of November.
Lest We Forget."

"I love you," said Frankie.

"I love you too," said Mother.

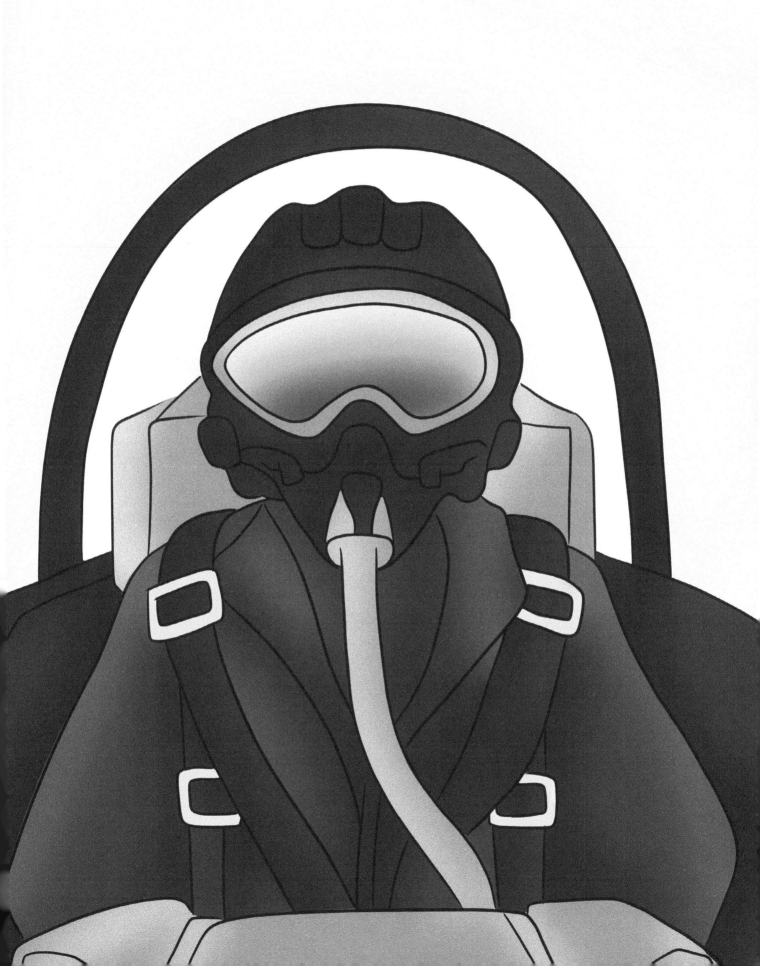

CPSIA information can be obtained
at www.ICGtesting.com
Printed in the USA
LVHW070435010921
696651LV00009B/182

9 781398 409316